Self-Confident Sandy

Sally Huss
with
Elizabeth Hamilton-Guarino

Sandy, Sandy, Self-Confident Sandy

Always keeps her mantra handy.

When her teacher asked her to tell a little bit about herself,
She proceeded to tell her classmates about her inner wealth.

"Some may wonder why I can do anything I try.

And the only answer can be: all these things are inside me."

Her classmates were stunned, as Sandy began rattling off
all the things she could do.
Was she just bragging, or was it true?

"I can run around a track…

And hike up a mountain with a pack.

I can make a friend when I meet someone new

By being interested in what they do.

I can help my mother prepare a dinner of salad and steak…

And follow it up with a delicious cake.

I can work hard on my lessons in school

And practice daily the Golden Rule."

Yes, this was correct and not a statement

of which anyone could object.

Everyone knew that she treated others

like she would like to be treated.

No, this was not a lie that she had created.

Sandy continued, "I can help a friend clean a closet

or rake some leaves

Without him even asking, 'Please?'

I can hit a ball with a bat...

And run the bases without losing my hat.

I can paint a picture and put it in a frame…

And hang it on the wall once I've signed my name.

I can read a book or even write a poem…

And read it to my grandma when I visit her at home.

I can be thankful for all that I have and can do.

I do this at home or while sitting in a pew.

I can dance…

and I can sing.

Yes, I can do most anything.

Once I set my mind and heart to it

I find that there is nothing to it, but to do it.

Still, I keep my mantra handy," explained Self-Confident Sandy.

Her classmates were thoroughly impressed

And were surprised when she had the boldness to suggest…

That they might do the same

And see how many things they could do and name.

Then altogether they sang:

"Some may wonder why I can do anything I try.

And the only answer can be: all these things are inside me."

"By trying and doing," said Sandy,

"That's how I can be the Best Ever Me.

You can do it too.

You can be the Best Ever You!"

The end, but not the end of being confident.

Sandy's Tips for Self-Appreciation

(Remember: little thoughts and words
of self-appreciation make a big difference to oneself.)

- Sometimes I pat myself on my back to tell me what a good job
I am doing.

- At other times I shake my hand with my other hand to thank
me for being helpful.

- Still other times I wrap my arms around myself to give myself
a hug for nothing more than being me.

Here are a few more books by Sally Huss that you might enjoy. They may be found on Amazon along with the rest of her extensive collection of books designed to delight and inspire!

At the end of this book you will find a Certificate of Merit that may be issued to any child who has fulfilled the requirements stated in the Certificate. This fine Certificate will easily fit into a 5"x7" frame, and happily suit any girl or boy who receives it!

Kind Words from Some Experts

"*Self-Confident Sandy* by Sally Huss with Elizabeth Hamilton-Guarino is awesome! This wonderful book has an important message for children about self-confidence and being able to show this self-confidence in very real-life ways. It is written in a way that all children will understand and it will make them smile and believe in themselves and how they can actively be in "life". Interestingly, this message of self-confidence, although written for children, also sends a very positive message for adults to embrace as well. *Self-Confident Sandy* sends a caring and loving message that ALL children are special and ALL children should celebrate this!"

-- Lynne M. Celli, PhD, Executive Director of Leadership and Professional Education, Endicott College, Beverly, MA

"*Sandy* is a gift, a gift for us to remember our inner greatness, being confident in what we love to do. This book is a MUST for our children to keep this confidence so that they do whatever they love to do, even in grown-up times. We adults can remember, with this book, our own childhood 'but I know that!' attitude of living and enjoying our time to be our best ever you."

-- Bernadette Bruckner, MA

"Love this book! An important message for all ages, even parents. Highly recommended for any classroom, office or home library".

-- Patty Maxwell, licensed Behavioral Specialist, Community Educator, Owner of Engage Kidz, LLC

"Love *Self-Confident Sandy*. Self-confidence cannot be taught, it's learned and earned from experience, which is why it's so important to encourage kids to be multi-disciplined and try new things!"

-- Skye Ostreicher, MPH, MA

"Confidence and Self-Esteem are required for any young girl to become a future leader. Self-Confidence Sandy is a delightful reminder that girls can find everything they need to succeed inside themselves. Get one for every girl you care about."

-- Beth Caldwell, Founder of Leadership Academy for Women, Author of *Women, LEAD!*

"*Self-Confident Sandy* is exactly what this world needs and Sally and Elizabeth delivered it! It is vital to teach our children well, and young, the value and the beauty that they are. This is a book I will definitely be sure to read often to my own children!"

-- Emily A. Francis, Msc.Ed, Author of *Whole Body Healing*

"Mindset Matters! *Self-Confident Sandy* knows how to celebrate all that she can do and all that she is. This delightful book encourages young readers to celebrate themselves, just like Sandy does."

-- Kris Fuller, CEO of Life Sparkles

"All parents just want their children to be happy and confident. *Self-Confident Sandy* is a positive, uplifting book for supporting healthy emotional development."

-- Sherianna Boyle, Author of *Emotional Detox*

"This book exemplifies the message we need our children to live! There is so much wisdom in being grounded and grateful for the gifts we have been given and to encourage others to do the same."

-- Kirsten Blackemore, Author of *Unleash Your Power*, Speaker, Success Coach

About the Contributors

Sally Huss

Author/Illustrator Sally Huss creates children's books to uplift the lives of children. She does this by giving them tools to overcome obstacles; by helping them value themselves and others; and by inspiring them to be the best that they can be. Her catalog of books now exceeds 100.

"Bright and happy," "light and whimsical" have been the catch phrases attached to the writings and art of Sally Huss for over 30 years. Sweet images dance across all of Sally's creations, whether in the form of children's books, paintings, wallpaper, ceramics, baby bibs, purses, clothing, or her King Features syndicated newspaper panel "Happy Musings."

Sally is a graduate of USC with a degree in Fine Art and through the years has had 26 of her own licensed art galleries throughout the world. sallyhuss.com.

Elizabeth Hamilton-Guarino

Elizabeth Hamilton-Guarino is one of America's foremost personal and corporate development consultants. She is the creator of The Best Ever You Network (or Best Ever You), a leading multimedia provider of lifestyle and self-help content. While participating in the Harvard Business School for Leadership program, Elizabeth serves as a Leadership Advisor for the Olympia Snowe Women's Leadership Institute.

In 2020 Elizabeth joined Sally Huss to create the best-selling children's book *A Lesson for Every Child: Learning About Food Allergies.* Living with life-threatening food allergies for many years, Elizabeth added her personal experience and her expertise to the project. She also sits on several boards of organizations and foundations that bring awareness to this life-threatening condition.

Elizabeth is also the best-selling author of *Percolate — Let Your Best Self Filter Through* (Hay House Publishing). elizabethguarino.com.

This certificate may be cut out, framed, and presented to any child who has earned it.

Certificate of Merit

_____
(Name)

The child named above is awarded this Certificate of Merit for:

*Making a daily effort to be the best that you can be

*Trusting yourself

*Daring to try something new

Presented by: _____ Date: _____

Made in the USA
Middletown, DE
17 April 2020